_b_oot

_h_at

_e_gg

_k_ite

_s_un

_P_enguin

More first letter sounds

Look at the pictures. The first letters (graphemes) are missing. Say the word, sound it out and write in the missing letter.

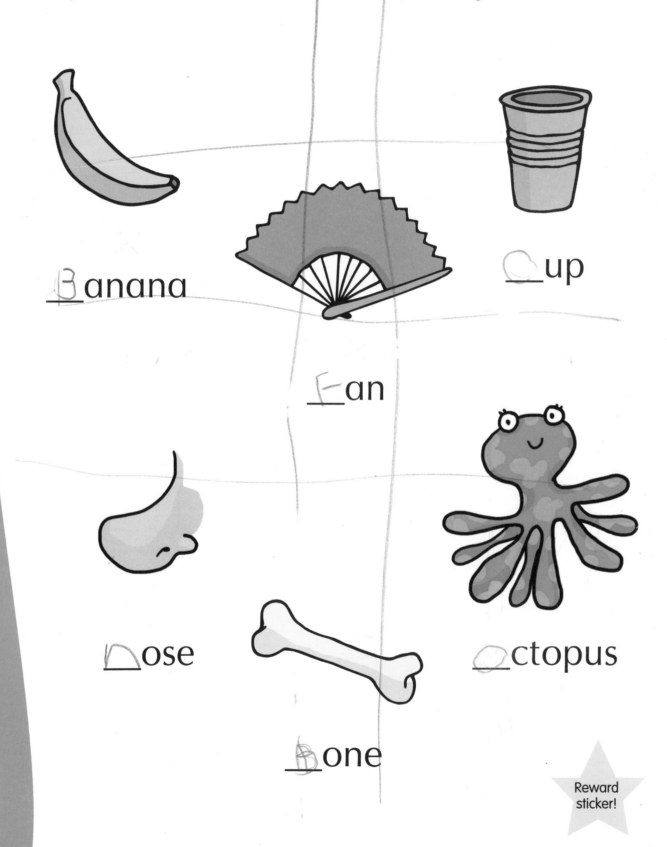

Banana

Fan

Cup

Nose

Octopus

Bone

Phonics

How to use this book with your child:

It is recommended that an adult spends time with a child while doing any kind of school practice, to offer encouragement and guidance. Find a quiet place to work, preferably at a table, and encourage your child to hold his or her pen or pencil correctly.

Try to work at your child's pace and avoid spending too long on any one page or activity. Most of all, emphasise the fun element of what you are doing and enjoy this special and exciting time!

Don't forget to add your reward sticker to each page you complete!

Reward sticker!

Designed by Plum5
Illustrations by Sue King, Sharon Smart and Andy Geeson
Educational consultant Chris Andrew

Autumn
Publishing

First letter sounds

Look at the pictures. The first letters (graphemes) are missing.
Say the word, sound it out and write in the missing letter.

_ant

_pan

_dog

_fish

_net

_rat

Reward
sticker!

Initial sounds

Look at the pictures. The first sounds are missing. These sounds are made up of two graphemes. Say the word, sound it out and write in the missing letters. You can choose from **ch**, **sh**, **qu** or **th**.

ch sh qu th

__ch__ick

__sh__ip

__qu__een

____ink

__ch__air

__sh__ark

5

End letter sounds

Look at the pictures. The last letters (graphemes) are missing. Say the word, sound it out and write in the missing letter.

ja<u>r</u>

fro<u>g</u>

mo<u>p</u>

ca<u>t</u>

hamste<u>r</u>

bir<u>d</u>

I did it!

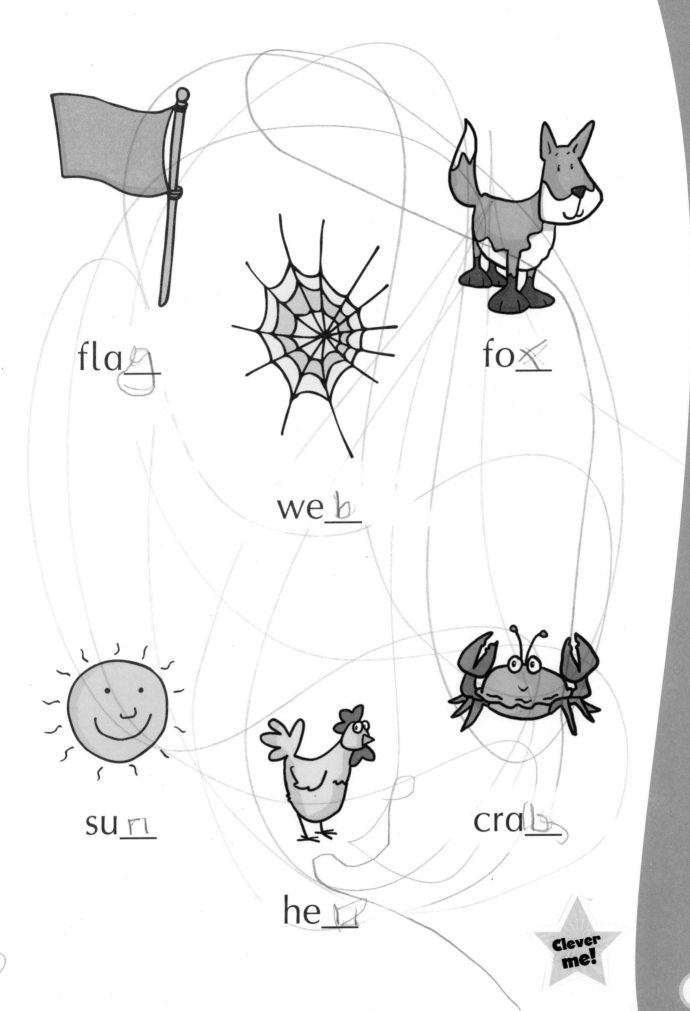

fla**g**

we **b**

fo**x**

su**n**

he **n**

cra**b**

More end letter sounds

Look at the pictures. The last letters (graphemes) are missing.
Say the word, sound it out and write in the missing letter.
You can choose from **nk** or **ng** or **ck**.

nk

ng

ck

ki___

dri___

ri___

cli___

thi___

First and last sounds

Look at the pictures. The first and last letters (graphemes) are missing.
Say the word, sound it out and write in the missing letters.

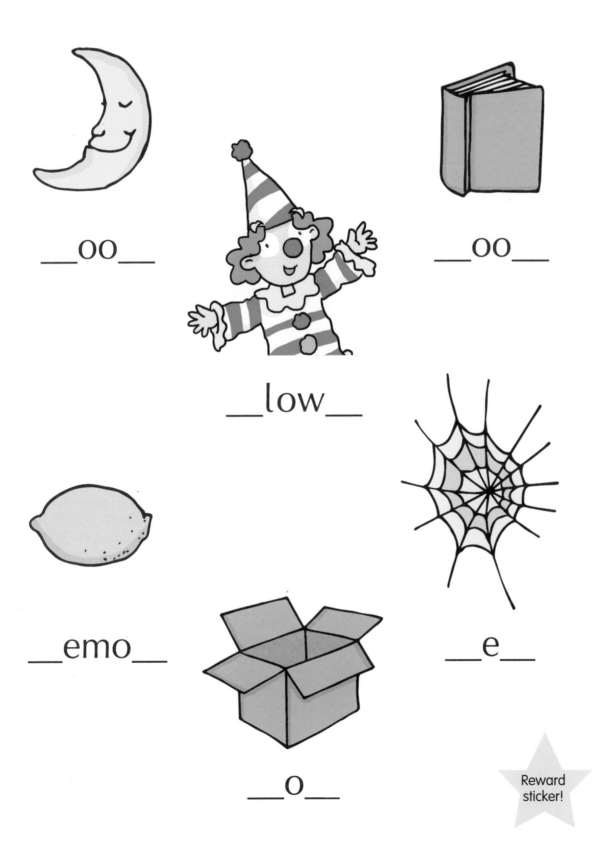

__oo__

__oo__

__low__

__emo__

__e__

__o__

Rhyming words

Rhyming words sound the same at the end of the words, like box and fox. Look at the pictures and the words underneath. Match the rhyming words together by drawing a line between them.

bat

clock

van

hat

king

pan

sock

wing

mug

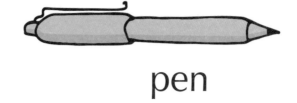

pen

10

ten

boy

frog

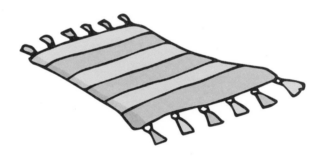

rug

toy

dog

Look at the pictures, say the word, sound it out and work out what the missing sound is. Write the letter in the space.

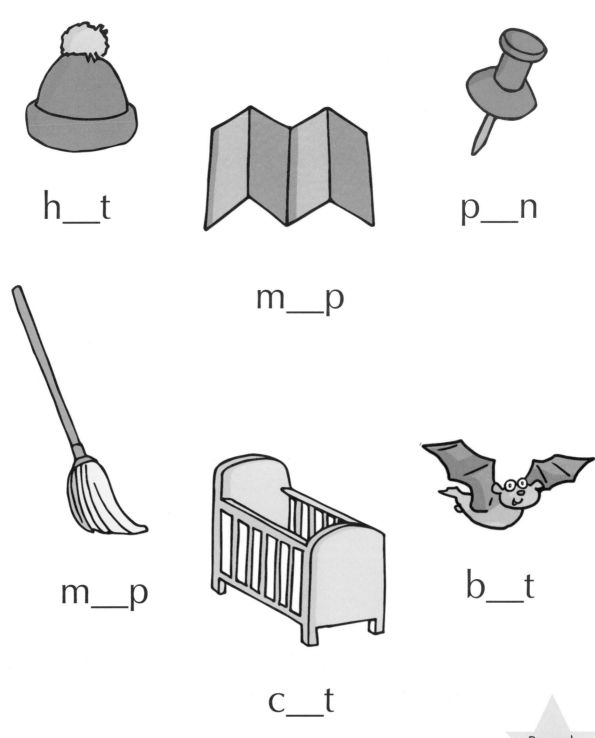

h__t

m__p

p__n

m__p

c__t

b__t

Reward sticker!

Brilliant blending

When two letters are put together to make one sound they are called a digraph. Fill in the blanks with the correct consonant blends. Choose from the tiles below.

fr   br   cr   cl   pl   fl   gl   gr   dr

___ead

___og

___y

___ant

___oud

___ock

___ue

___ab

___ush

Reward sticker!

More brilliant blending

Fill in the blanks with the correct consonant blends.
Choose from the tiles below.

st

sn

cr

cl

gr

ch

fl

dr

___air

___ick

___ink

___air

___own

___owman

___ower

___um

___apes

Reward
sticker!

Amazing ending blending

Fill in the blanks at the end of the word with the correct consonant blends. Choose from the tiles below.

ck

nd

mp

sh

lk

nt

fi___

du___

te___

ha___

clo___

sta___

mi___

la___

a___

Reward sticker!

Playing in the rain

Look at the words below. You can choose either **ay** or **ai** to go in the missing spaces:

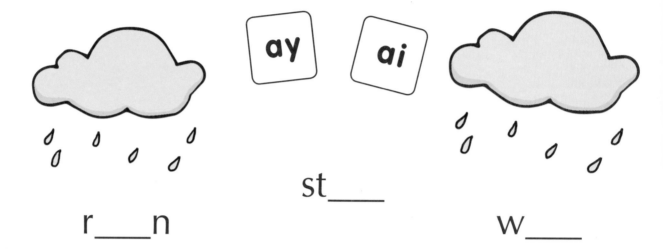

r___n

st___

w___

tr___n

d___

p___nt

pl___

w___t

tr___

Get a fright

What three letters make the sound i? **igh** makes a sound like a long i. Make these words make sense by adding **igh**.

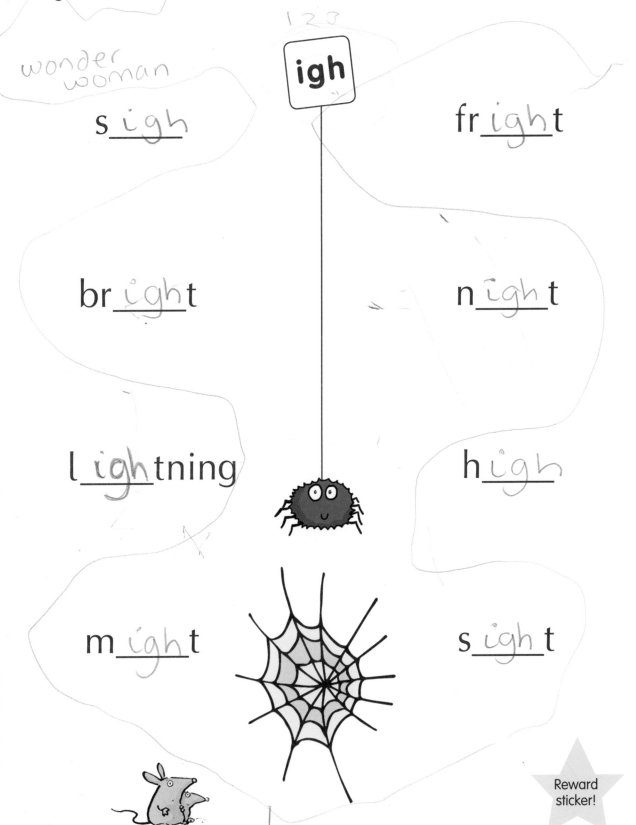

wonder woman

s_igh_

fr_igh_t

br_igh_t

n_igh_t

l_igh_tning

h_igh_

m_igh_t

s_igh_t

17

Ar or or?

Draw lines from the pictures to the correct sound (digraph).
Write the words in the correct box.

ar

star
car
Jar

or

corn
thorn
Fork

Reward
sticker!

Air or ir?

Write the correct sounds into the words below.

air   ir

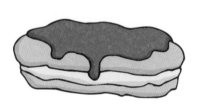

st___

f___

b___d

ecl___

ch___

g___l

Sound out

Circle the pictures that make the sound **ou** like in house.

Ou or ow?

Draw lines from the pictures to the correct sound (digraph).
Write the words in the correct box.

OU

OW

Oy or oi?

Draw lines from the pictures to the correct sound (digraph).

oi

oy

Reward sticker!

Ow or oa?

Look at the pictures below. Find the words from the word bank that match these pictures, and write them in the correct boxes.

a.

b.

c.

d.

e.

f.

arrow

window

goat

coach

snow

coat

Are you sure?

Read the words out loud, choose one from each group and draw a picture of it in the frame.

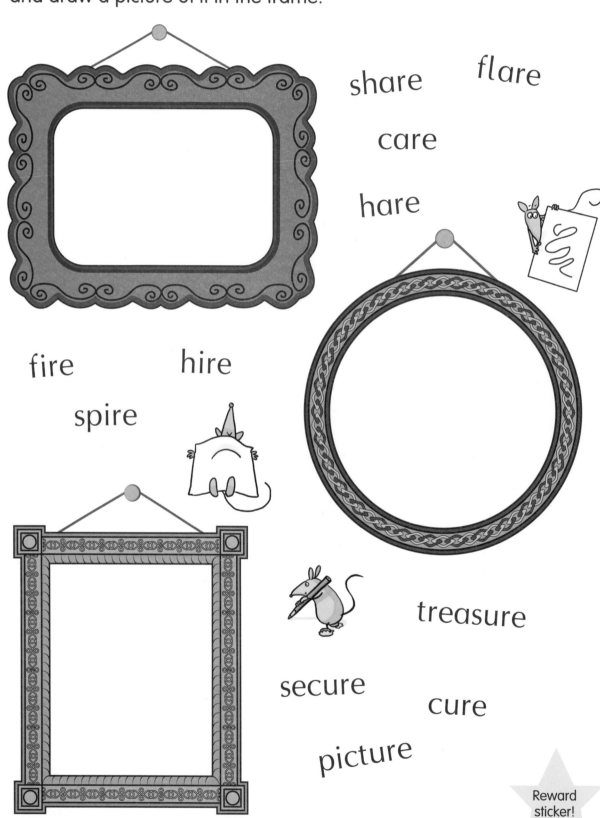

share

flare

care

hare

fire

hire

spire

treasure

secure

cure

picture

Atten-shun!

Words ending with **tion** as in nation sound like (shun).
Words ending with **sion** as in vision also sound like (shun).
Find words ending in these sounds in the word search below.

r	i	s	e	c	t	i	o	n	k
e	x	v	r	i	g	e	q	d	v
a	i	y	j	a	i	m	i	z	s
c	o	n	f	e	s	s	i	o	n
t	i	l	l	u	s	i	o	n	x
i	a	d	d	i	t	i	o	n	h
o	d	e	c	i	s	i	o	n	f
n	s	t	a	t	i	o	n	k	c
o	u	s	e	s	s	i	o	n	v
t	n	f	b	y	c	x	p	k	d

section   confession   reaction

station   illusion   decision

addition   session

Reward
sticker!

Happy endings

Lion

Colour in the correct spelling to end each sentence, and then write it in the space provided.

Listen! I need your full _____

attenshun	attencian
attention	attenshon

If you don't understand,
you ask for an _____

explanasion	explanacian
explanashun	explanation

Another way of
saying adding is _____

addician	addition
addision	addishun

Fireworks are like an _____

exploshun

explotion

explosion

explocian

If you bump in
to someone this
can be called a _____

collision

collishun

collition

collician

If you say that someone
can do something, you
have given them _____

permition

permician

permishun

permission

Reward
sticker!

You're the teacher!

Look at the sentences below. Which are correct?
Give them a ✔ if they are correct or circle any mistakes
and write the correct word beneath.

a. England is a nation.

b. Is there anything good
on televition?

c. It is my ambision to be a writer.

d. When are you going to
the station?

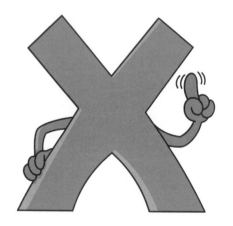

e. Illutions are my favourite type of magic.

Reward
sticker!

No nonsense!

Using the consonant blends below and some vowels make up some nonsense words that might describe a fruit.
You might describe how they look, taste, smell or feel!

e.g. That apple smells **flurpy** or that pear tastes **glucky**!

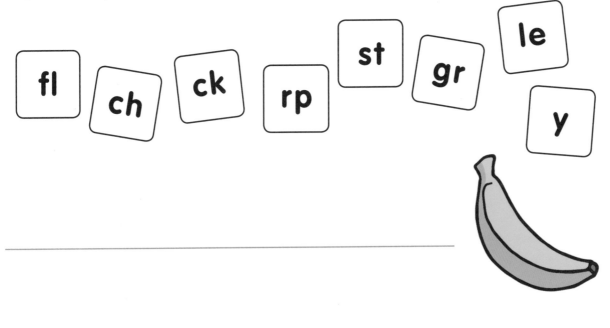

Reward sticker!

Nonsense words

Circle the words below which are nonsense words.
Then pick your favourite nonsense word and draw a picture
of it in the frame opposite!

robot

kear

vurk

queen

boot

kite

chick

queck

jigh

thorden

zurd

coat

duck

nud

kitten

flurp

plab

Reward
sticker!

Reward
sticker!

Answers

First letter sounds

<u>a</u>nt, <u>p</u>an, <u>d</u>og, <u>f</u>ish, <u>n</u>et, <u>r</u>at, <u>b</u>oot, <u>h</u>at, <u>e</u>gg, <u>k</u>ite, <u>s</u>un, <u>p</u>enguin

More first letter sounds

<u>b</u>anana, <u>f</u>an, <u>c</u>up, <u>n</u>ose, <u>b</u>one, <u>o</u>ctopus

Initial sounds

<u>ch</u>ick, <u>sh</u>ip, <u>qu</u>een, <u>th</u>ink, <u>ch</u>air, <u>sh</u>ark

End letter sounds

ja<u>r</u>, fro<u>g</u>, mo<u>p</u>, hamste<u>r</u>, ca<u>t</u>, bir<u>d</u>, fla<u>g</u>, we<u>b</u>, fo<u>x</u>, su<u>n</u>, he<u>n</u>, cra<u>b</u>

More end letter sounds

ki<u>ng</u>, dri<u>nk</u>, ri<u>ng</u>, cli<u>ck</u>, thi<u>nk</u>

First and last sounds

<u>moon</u>, <u>clown</u>, <u>book</u>, <u>lemon</u>, <u>box</u>, <u>web</u>

Rhyming words

bat - hat, clock - sock, van - pan, king - wing, mug - rug, pen - ten, frog - dog, toy - boy

Middle letter sounds

h<u>a</u>t, m<u>a</u>p, p<u>i</u>n, m<u>o</u>p, c<u>o</u>t, b<u>a</u>t

Brilliant blending

<u>br</u>ead, <u>fr</u>og, <u>fl</u>y, <u>pl</u>ant, <u>cl</u>oud, <u>cl</u>ock, <u>gl</u>ue, <u>cr</u>ab, <u>br</u>ush

More brilliant blending

<u>ch</u>air, <u>cl</u>ick, <u>dr</u>ink, <u>st</u>air, <u>cr</u>own, <u>sn</u>owman, <u>fl</u>ower, <u>dr</u>um, <u>gr</u>apes

Amazing ending blending

fi<u>sh</u>, du<u>ck</u>, ten<u>t</u>, han<u>d</u>, clo<u>ck</u>, sta<u>mp</u>, mi<u>lk</u>, la<u>mp</u>, a<u>nt</u>

Playing in the rain

r<u>ai</u>n, st<u>ay</u>, w<u>ay</u>, d<u>ay</u>, tr<u>ai</u>n, p<u>ai</u>nt, w<u>ai</u>t, pl<u>ay</u>, tr<u>ay</u>

Get a fright

s<u>igh</u>, fr<u>igh</u>t, br<u>igh</u>t, n<u>igh</u>t, l<u>igh</u>tning, h<u>igh</u>, m<u>igh</u>t, s<u>igh</u>t

Ar or or?

ar st<u>ar</u>, c<u>ar</u>, j<u>ar</u>
or c<u>or</u>n, f<u>or</u>k, th<u>or</u>n

Air or ir?

air st<u>air</u>, f<u>air</u>, ecl<u>air</u>, ch<u>air</u>
ir b<u>ir</u>d, g<u>ir</u>l

Sound out

h<u>ou</u>se, m<u>ou</u>se

Ou or ow?

ou cl<u>ou</u>d, h<u>ou</u>se, m<u>ou</u>se
ow cl<u>ow</u>n, cr<u>ow</u>n, fl<u>ow</u>er

Oy or oi?

oy b<u>oy</u>, t<u>oy</u>
oi p<u>oi</u>nt, c<u>oi</u>n, f<u>oi</u>l, t<u>oi</u>let

Ow or oa?

a. sn<u>ow</u>, **b.** c<u>oa</u>ch, **c.** arr<u>ow</u>, **d.** wind<u>ow</u>, **e.** g<u>oa</u>t **f.** c<u>oa</u>t

Atten-shun!

r	i	s	e	c	t	i	o	n	k
e	x	v	r	i	g	e	q	d	v
a	i	y	j	a	i	m	i	z	s
c	o	n	f	e	s	s	i	o	n
t	i	l	l	u	s	i	o	n	x
i	a	d	d	i	t	i	o	n	h
o	d	e	c	i	s	i	o	n	f
n	s	t	a	t	i	o	n	k	c
o	u	s	e	s	s	i	o	n	v
t	n	f	b	y	c	x	p	k	d

Happy endings

Listen! I need your full **attention**.
If you don't understand, you ask for an **explanation**.
Another way of saying adding is **addition**.
Fireworks are like an **explosion**.
If you bump in to someone this can be called a **collision**.
If you say that someone can do something, you have given them **permission**.

You're the teacher!

Correct **a d**
b. televition - television
c. ambision - ambition
e. Illutions - Illusions

Nonsense words

vurk, kear, queck, jigh, zurd, thorden, nud, flurp, plab